Text copyright © 2004 Anna Neil
Illustration copyright © 2004 Germano Ovani

The right of Anna Neil and Germano Ovani to be identified as the
author and illustrator of this work respectively has been asserted by
them in accordance with the Copyright, Designs and Patents Act, 1988.

Little Peculiars is a trade mark of Keppel Publishing Ltd.
This edition published 2004.   ISBN: 1 904827 20 9
A CIP catalogue record for this book is available from
the British Library.

Printed in Singapore

Keppel Publishing Limited
The Grey House, Kenbridge Road,
New Galloway, DG7 3RP Scotland.

A BUNCH OF PECULIARS

By Anna Neil

Illustrated by Germano Ovani

KEPPEL  PUBLISHING

IDIOSYNCRATIC EARS

THE BUTTERFLY WINGS

THE MAN with butterfly wings for ears has often tried to fly. But, of course, being too heavy he inevitably fails, and has ended up in hospital on numerous occasions. The nurses, however, are always delighted each time he is admitted. They have never had a patient with softer, more lovable ears. His delicate ears also smell of sandalwood so, whenever the nurses tend to him, he wafts the heady scent in their adoring faces. ❀

THE VASES

A BEAUTY in full bloom, the young lady with vase ears naturally receives many flowers from her admirers. She always knows just where to put them, and she knows just what she likes. As a baby she insisted upon snowdrops. As a girl she desired sweet peas and then, as a teenager, black tulips made of plastic. Now she has come to realise that her ears were made to hold nothing but *Columbian Monte Vista* orchids.

THE CHAIRS

THE EARS of this little boy provide his consciences with a convenient place to sit. Being that his consciences are quite different in personality, his ears have gradually evolved to accommodate these distinctions. One of his ears is a section from a church pew, the other is an armchair with a remote control on one arm and a bag of chips on the other. One conscience sits praying that the little boy will stay out of trouble, while the other conscience has no need for such soul searching. All he has to do is nudge the boy's cheek occasionally and point to the source of impending temptation. ❦

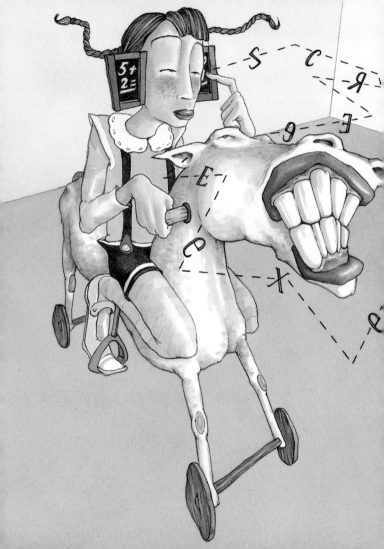

THE BLACKBOARDS

THE CHILD with blackboards for ears is terribly unpopular. The reason for this is that her ears often become itchy and she has no qualms whatsoever about scratching them in public!

THE BRIEFCASES

IT IS extremely useful for this young student to have briefcases for ears. He can open and close them at will, depending on whether or not he wishes to listen. He has the added advantage of being able to put things into them, such as lecture notes, or important messages his mother wants him to remember. Usually, however, if he puts them in his left ear, within an hour or two they somehow manage to get into his right ear, only to flutter away the next time he opens it. ❧

ECCENTRIC NOSES

THE RAINBOW

THE LADY with a rainbow nose can often seem blissfully content. On first glance, a passerby may say to himself, *"What's she so happy about?"* Then he will see her nose - and more importantly the marvellous glistening thing dangling from the end of it - and he will know. Indeed he may wish that he too had treasure ahead of him wherever he went. You see, this divine creature has a pot of gold at the end of her nose. Some would follow it to the end of the earth but she is happy just knowing it is there.

THE GRAMOPHONE

THE MOST distinguished nose,
and the perfect nose through which
to hum old-time melodies. Ladies simply
love the man with a gramophone nose,
provided he does not sneeze. On a final
note, his funnel-shaped proboscis is
excellent for smelling subtly
perfumed roses. ❧

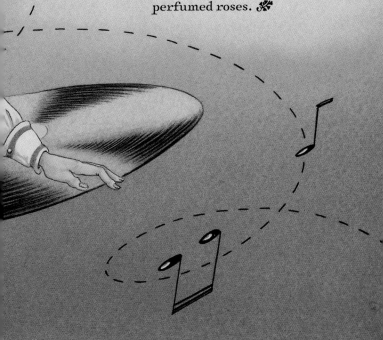

THE CURLING-TONGS

UNDERSTANDABLY, THE lady with the curling-tongs nose always has the same hairstyle. She feels it is the hairstyle that nature meant her to have. Her hair is naturally straight but each morning, after uncurling from her bed, she uses her nose to turn the bottom half of her hair into ringlets (the top of her hair does not reach her nose). The effect of this is very pretty and rather Jane Austin in appearance. A gentleman's first impression of her might be, *"My, what a romantic looking lady."* And then when he sees her nose he might exclaim, *"And practical too!"* ✸

THE JIGSAW PIECE

LIFE CAN be difficult for the young man with the jigsaw-piece nose. He cannot walk down the street without someone trying to take his nose from under his... ...eyes, believing it to be the last missing piece of their favourite jigsaw puzzle. ❀

THE UMBRELLA

MOST LADIES would love to wear lashings of super shiny, extra luscious, water-soluble lipstick. Very few would dare, however, for fear of the unthinkable consequences if the heavens were suddenly to open. Happily it is a different story altogether for the lady lucky enough to have an umbrella for a nose.

BESPOKE MOUTHS

THE OYSTER

THE LADY with the oyster mouth never has to work. Yet, she has all the money she needs to buy all the diamonds and champagne she craves. Every few days one of her tonsils dislodges itself from the back of her throat, rolls down her tongue and on to her complacent palm. She then sells it to a rich merchant for quite a bit more than the average pensioner's yearly allowance. Since her mouth is an oyster, her tonsils, naturally, are pearls. When asked if she ever wears her pearls on a necklace she usually replies, a trifle indignantly, *"Certainly not! Would you wear your tonsils around your neck?"*

THE BROKEN ZIP

THIS POOR chap prefers not to leave the house
if he can help it. His mouth is a broken zip.
He used to be able to open and close his mouth
with a perfect glide. But as a youth, while all
the others were breaking their noses, he
decided to break his mouth. He did it
himself with a pair of pliers. He regrets
sometimes doing this now, for he has
come to realise that the world is a
dangerous place for someone with a
mouth that cannot close.

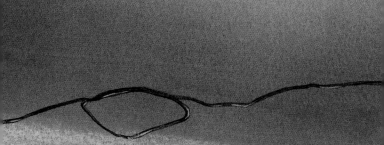

THE TEACUP

LOVELORN AND unassuming, this sweet old lady, quite conveniently, has a teacup for a mouth. With a little delicate manoeuvring it can come in very handy whenever one guest too many arrives for tea. Her mouth is also useful for catching her tears, as she watches an excessive number of weepy movies. So, in only a week, she usually manages to save enough tears to make a generous portion of very tasty salty soup.

THE PIANO KEYS

WHAT A delightful gentleman to have with you on a train journey, when the child is screaming and the old ladies' gossip is becoming tedious. He does not say very much, so he will neither give the mother some know-it-all advice, nor join in the old ladies' gossip. Instead he will simply open his mouth and begin gently tapping on his teeth and the lovely lullaby that emerges will soothe the baby until she is sound asleep. Then he will tap his teeth a little harder and play old music-hall favourites, to which the old ladies will immediately start dancing. Up and down the aisle of the carriage they will waltz, and all will be marvellously entertained. 🎕

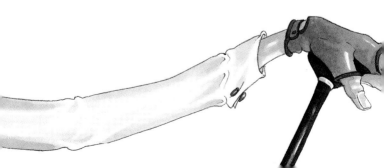

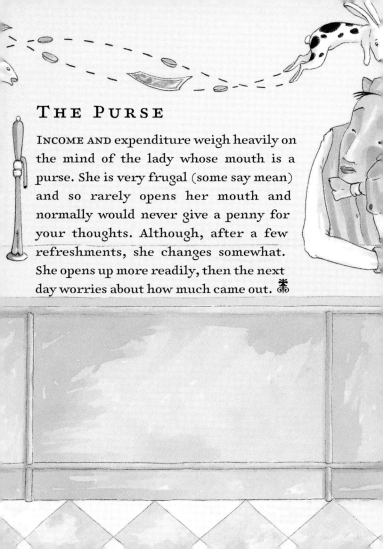

THE PURSE

INCOME AND expenditure weigh heavily on the mind of the lady whose mouth is a purse. She is very frugal (some say mean) and so rarely opens her mouth and normally would never give a penny for your thoughts. Although, after a few refreshments, she changes somewhat. She opens up more readily, then the next day worries about how much came out. ✤